My First...
School Trip

First published in the UK in 2009 by
QED Publishing
A Quarto Group Company
226 City Road
London EC1V 2TT
www.qed-publishing.co.uk

A catalogue record for this book is available
from the British Library.

ISBN 978 1 84835 162 2

Author Eve Marleau
Illustrator Michael Garton
Consultants Shirley Bickler and Tracey Dils
Designer Elaine Wilkinson

Publisher Steve Evans
Creative Director Zeta Davies
Managing Editor Amanda Askew

Printed and bound in China

The words in **bold** are
explained in the glossary
on page 24.

My First...
School Trip

Eve Marleau and Michael Garton

QED Publishing

Today is Emily's school trip to the park. "Hello Mrs Clark!" says Emily as they walk towards the bus.

"Hello Emily. Are you looking forward to seeing the animals and plants that live in the park?"

"Oh yes!"

The bus goes up hills…

and through towns.

Finally, Emily sees
a big, brown sign. 5

At the park centre, the children meet **Ranger** Roberts.
He looks after the park and all its animals and plants.

"Before we start exploring, here are the three rules of the park."

"Pick up your **litter**, stay close to an adult, and most importantly, respect the animals. This is their home."

7

"Let's start exploring!"

"What animals and plants are we looking for today for our **wall display**?"

Oak trees

Ducks

The children start
to walk around the
park. They walk
past a pond.

"Look, there's a duck! I'm going
to draw it for my project."

They walk through a wooded area.

"Mrs Clark, I can see a butterfly! I'm going to draw a picture of one."

"Look, there are some acorns on the ground," says Emily.

"I'll collect them to stick on the wall."

At lunchtime, the children sit in the **picnic area**.

Mrs Clark hands out packed lunches to the class.

"Remember class, never leave litter
or food in the park. It is bad for the
environment, and the animals, too."

After lunch, Ranger Roberts
takes the children to the pond.

"Ponds are home to many animals.
Do you know which ones?"

"Geese live on ponds. I can see a mummy goose and her babies," says Emily.

"Frogs live in ponds. They lay eggs called **frogspawn**," says Amy.

"Fish live in ponds, too. I have goldfish in my pond at home," says James.

17

"Children, find a place to sit on the grass. Then you can draw any of the plants or animals that you have seen today."

Back at the park centre,
the children talk about
what they have seen.

"I picked some grass to add
to my picture of the pond."

"I drew a picture of the
mummy goose and her
babies. I'm going to add
twigs to the picture!"

"I saw a squirrel run up a tree. I'm going to stick acorns around my picture because squirrels eat acorns," says Emily.

Back at school, the children finish their pictures.

Mrs Clark
puts them up
on the wall.

"Well done everyone.

Your pictures
look lovely!"

23

Glossary

Environment The land, air and water that surround us.

Frogspawn The eggs of frogs.

Litter Waste or rubbish that is left in a public area.

Picnic area A special place in public spaces where people can eat and drink.

Ranger A person who looks after a park or area of the countryside.

Wall display A group of pictures or posters that are stuck on a wall.